OFFICIALLY NOTED

10/18 Book stained from inside back cover. ym

LYDIA MARIA CHILD

Over the River
and Through the Wood

ILLUSTRATED BY DAVID CATROW

SCHOLASTIC INC.
New York Toronto London Auckland Sydney

ISBN 0-590-63578-6

Illustrations copyright © 1996 by David Catrow. All rights reserved. Published by Scholastic Inc., 555 Broadway, New York, NY 10012, by arrangement with Henry Holt and Company, Inc. SCHOLASTIC and associated logos are trademarks and/or registered trademarks of Scholastic Inc.

12 11 10 9 8 7 6 5 4 3 2 1   8 9/9 0 1 2 3/0

Printed in the U.S.A.   14

First Scholastic printing, November 1998

To Kirby,
my best friend
—D. C.

Over the river and through
the wood,
To grandfather's house we go;

The horse knows the way
To carry the sleigh
Through the white and drifted snow.

Over the river and through the wood—
Oh, how the wind does blow!
It stings the toes
And bites the nose,

As over the ground we go.

Over the river and through the wood,
To have a first-rate play.

Hear the bells ring,
"Ting-a-ling-ding!"

Hurrah for Thanksgiving Day!

Over the river and through the wood
Trot fast, my dapple-gray!

Spring over the ground,
Like a hunting hound!
For this is Thanksgiving Day.

Over the river and through the wood,
And straight through the barnyard gate

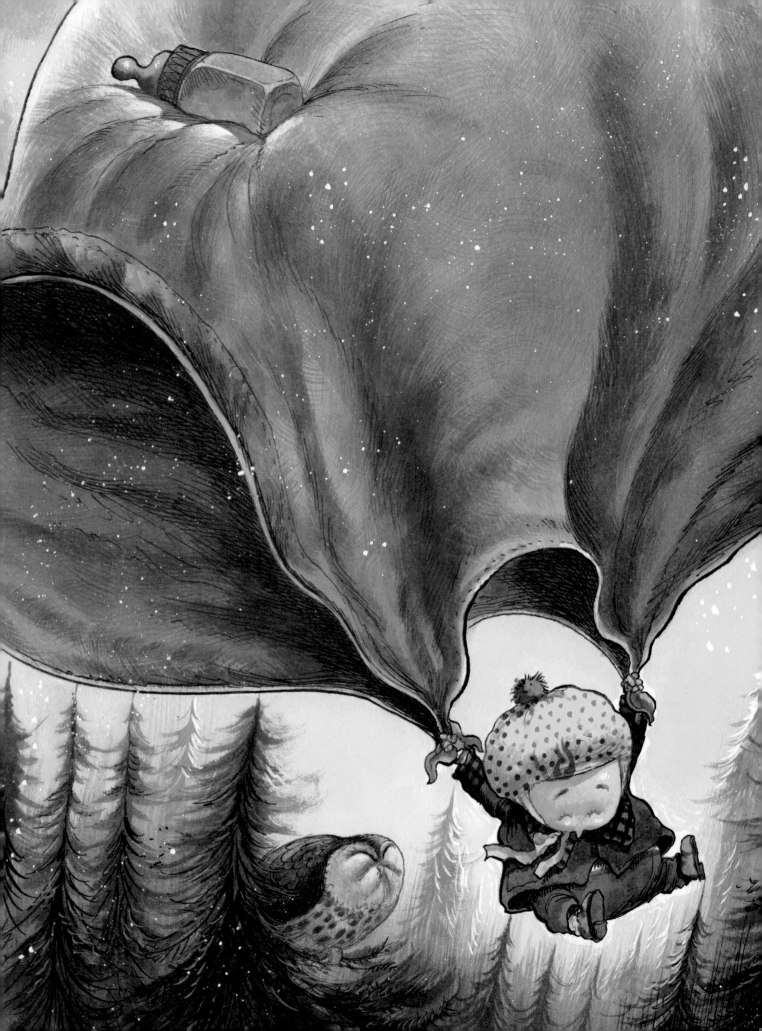

We seem to go
Extremely slow—
It is so hard to wait!

**Over the river and through the wood—
Now grandmother's cap I spy!**

Hurrah for the fun!

Is the pudding done?

Hurrah for the pumpkin pie!